How to Grow *Super* Soybeans

by Dr. Harold Willis

Drawings and photographs are by the author

Copyright © 1989 by Harold L. Willis
All rights reserved.

Designed and produced by *Acres U.S.A.,*
P.O. Box 9547, Kansas City, Missouri

ISBN 0-911311-21-1
Library of Congress Catalog card number
89-085541

Printed in the United States of America

How to Grow *Super* Soybeans

by Dr. Harold Willis

CONTENTS

FOREWORD

How would you like to grow high quality crops while improving your soil and *reducing* your expenses? How would you like to receive premium prices for your crops or else grow your own feed that helps keep your animals healthy and high-producing? How would you like to grow lush, disease-free crops in a drought year while your neighbor's fields turn brown and shrivel?

Sound like a dream? It *can* be done, and it IS being done by an increasing number of farmers who have discovered that working *with* laws of nature and using beneficial soil organisms can make farming enjoyable, satisfying and profitable.

There are no magic or secret ingredients involved, just common sense farming. Nothing fancy. What counts is the bottom line.

True, you may have to change the way you do things. You may have to try something new (but has the old way given you the results you want?). It may even be a little more trouble, but aren't high quality and "doing it right" worth it?

To be frank, the standard chemical-intensive methods of modern agriculture are depleting our soil, poisoning our environment, and producing low quality "foodless food" besides.

There are simpler and better ways to grow food. They do not pollute, and they use living soil organisms to help grow vigorous, healthy crops that are naturally resistant to diseases and pests. And, believe it or not, properly balanced soil will actually *discourage* most weeds. The principles outlined in this book apply to any crop, but we will especially see how you can grow SUPER soybeans!

CHAPTER 1

The Amazing Soybean

The soybean is a truly amazing and versatile crop plant. It is one of the oldest food plants, domesticated by 1100 BC in northeastern China. Its ancestor is a wild vine-like plant which produces tiny, hard seeds that are useless for food unless properly prepared.

Over the next several hundred years the domesticated soybean (called *Glycine max* by botanists) spread throughout much of eastern Asia. It grew upright and yielded larger, more digestible seeds. A variety of foods was developed from the soybean, ranging from soybean sprouts to steamed raw beans to roasted seeds to soy milk to soy sauce to fermented soybean paste and cake to soy flour to the commonly eaten curd called tofu (or doufu).

Soybeans reached the western world by the early 1700s and were first grown in North America by 1804. Benjamin Franklin appears to have been involved in introducing soybeans from France to Philadelphia at that time. A number of varieties was grown and evaluated in the United States during the 1800s. The primary use for the crop was for forage, hay and green manure.

In the 1880s, French scientists discovered that the soybean contains practically no starch, so its use in diabetic diets began. Later its high protein content was recognized.

Modern uses. In the early 1900s the first processing of seeds for oil and meal was done in England. For the most part, soybeans were a neglected crop until World War II. Germany developed a soy oil lard substitute and a meat substitute. In the U.S. increasing amounts of soybean meal were used as livestock and poultry feed, especially after 1945, when consumption of meat increased dramatically. More recently, an increasing proportion of American soybean production has been used by the food processing industry—in such foods as margarine, shortening, ice cream, salad dressings and mayonnaise. Industry uses lesser amounts, in products including paint, ink, putty, caulking, wallpaper, rubber substitutes, adhesives, fire extinguisher foam, electrical insulation and gasoline. The versatile soybean is a part of everyone's life in developed countries.

At present, most soybeans (over three-fourths of the world supply) are grown in the United States (especially in the corn belt and Mississippi Valley), in Brazil and Argentina. China produces most of the soybeans grown in the Orient, while only a few are grown in Europe. In the U.S., the soybean is third in production (corn and wheat are first and second) and second in value (corn is first) of crops grown.

Growth and development. In order to best manage soybean production, one needs an understanding of how the plant grows and develops.

Germination. After being planted in the soil, the seed absorbs moisture, changing from less than 13% moisture to about 50% in several hours. After one or two days the first root (called the radicle) emerges through the seed coat and begins growing downward to establish the root system.

The upper part of the young plant (the hypocotyl) begins to lengthen, pulling the remainder of the seed upward. About five to fifteen days after planting, the new plant arches through the soil, and the oval seed leaves (cotyledons) open up. The cotyledons provide the seedling with food (that was stored in them) for about a week, plus they soon turn green and begin making a little additional food by photosynthesis. Later they drop off.

Seed germination and emergence is a critical period in the life of a soybean because poor emergence due to a soil crust, cold temperatures or seedling pests or diseases can drastically cut yield.

Vegetative growth. After the seedling has emerged from the soil, the young stem and first leaves begin to rapidly grow upward. The seedling is very tough and frost resistant. If the terminal bud (growing tip) of the stem is killed, side buds will take over.

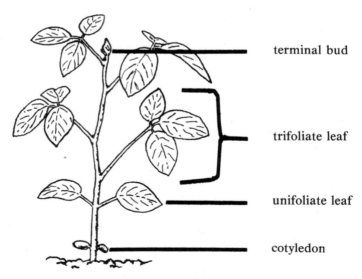

A young soybean plant showing several parts.

After emergence, for the first six to eight weeks, the soybean grows its stem (and possibly branches) and leaves. This is called the *vegetative period.*

The first two leaves that develop are called unifoliates, meaning that the leaf has a single flat surface, the blade, similar to the leaves of elm or maple trees. The remaining leaves are three-bladed, or trifoliates. Here, the total leaf has three divisions, all attached to a single "leaf stalk," or petiole. The place where a leaf petiole attaches to the stem is called a node. Later, flowers will develop at the nodes, between the petiole and stem, and branches also grow out from here.

After the first few leaves develop, overall growth of the plant increases rapidly. If plants are spaced far apart, more side branches will grow outward to capture as much light as possible, producing a bushy-looking plant. Plants in dense stands tend to grow upward, with few or no branches. Some soybean varieties tend to branch more than others.

As new upper leaves begin to shade older, lower leaves, the lower leaves may turn yellow and fall off. This is nothing to be concerned about, since the plant is just getting rid of unproductive leaves.

Roots. While the stem and leaves are growing upward, the root system is growing deeper into the soil. At first, the plant grows a main taproot, but soon side roots branch off, and still others grow off from them. The deepest

The same variety will produce erect or branched plants depending on plant population, ranging from 14 (left) to 12 (center) to 8 plants per foot (right).

roots may reach down five feet or more in loose, well drained soil, but most of the roots are found in the upper one foot of soil.

The young roots start to develop root nodules within a week after emergence if the proper nitrogen-fixing bacteria are present in the soil. The nitrogen-fixing nodule bacteria, technically called *Rhizobium,* enter the nodules and after ten to fourteen days are able to supply most of the plant's nitrogen needs, if the nodules are healthy. In favorable soil conditions, a couple dozen or so pea-sized nodules will develop on the upper roots of a plant. Healthy nodules will be pink or reddish inside.

Flowering. In typical soybean plants, after six to ten trifoliate leaves have grown, the next main stage in the plant's life begins, the *reproductive period.* From 3 to 15 flower buds develop at each node of the stem.

There are two main types of soybean, depending on how flowering occurs. Varieties called *indeterminate* continue growing upward at the tip of the stem for several weeks after flowering begins lower on the stem. Upper nodes will not flower until later. Most commercial varieties are indeterminate. They typically grow taller and do best in short growing seasons.

A few varieties are called *determinate* and complete their growth in height first, then all flowers bloom at about the same time. They are usually one-half to two-thirds as tall as indeterminate varieties and so are often called "semidwarfs." There are also some intermediate varieties, called *semideterminate,* which grow taller during the first part of their flowering period.

The flowers of soybean are tiny (¼ inch) and white, pink or purple. They resemble the flowers of pea or clover, since the soybean is in the same plant family, the legume family. Many more flowers are produced than eventually produce seed pods. The extras drop off, anywhere from 50 to 80% of the total.

The flowers are self-pollinated; that is, the flower fertilizes itself, and insects are not required to carry pollen from one flower to another.

The light factor. The beginning of the flowering period is hastened by higher temperatures and a greater amount of vegetative growth, but a major-factor that controls flowering is photoperiod—the length of the day. Flowering of a certain variety begins sooner when the days are shorter and later when the days are longer (if the plants are grown where there is artificial light during the night, they may never flower).

Each variety is adapted to flower and complete its life cycle at a certain geographic latitude (distance from the equator). Normally, if planted in the spring, the plants will begin flowering in mid-summer, after the days begin to get longer (in the northern hemisphere, the longest day, the summer solstice, is about June 21). But the days are longer the closer one gets to the pole (the sun never sets above the arctic circle during the summer). This means that if you try to grow a variety adapted to a certain latitude, say around St. Louis, Missouri, at more northerly locations, say Minneapolis, Minnesota, the days will be longer and the plants will not begin to flower until later, and they may not mature before frost. If grown to the south, they will mature too soon and yield will be reduced.

Therefore, soybean varieties are grouped into 13 maturity groups, depending on the climate and latitude for which they are adapted. These maturity groups are given numbers, with numbers 000, 00, 0 and I being adapted to Canada and the northern United States, and numbers VII, VIII and IX being grown in the southern U.S. (Group X is tropical.) Be certain to plant a variety adapted to your area.

Pod development. One or two weeks after the first flowers, the first seed pods appear, with most pods being set within the next three weeks. Inside the pod, three (or sometimes four) tiny seeds begin to grow and develop.

For the next 30 to 40 days, the seeds rapidly fill with food produced in the leaves. The seed-filling period is the most critical in the life of the soybean plant with regard to yield. If weather conditions are adverse, such as drought stress or leaf loss from hail, yields will be cut severely. At this time, the plant takes 30 to 40% of its total mineral needs from the soil, so soil fertility should be at a peak.

After most seeds have filled, the growth activities of the plant rather suddenly slow down (called *senescence*). The leaves slow down their photosynthesis and begin to turn yellow, eventually dropping off. Root nodules cease producing nitrogen.

Maturity. The newly formed seeds contain about 90% moisture. As the seeds fill with food, moisture content decreases to about 60 to 65%. When seeds are mature (filled), the moisture content is 45 to 55% and the pods and stems of the plant are yellow or brown. The mature seed itself will also be completely yellow when mature (if it is a yellow-seeded variety).

In warm, dry weather, seed moisture will continue to drop to about 13 to 14%, when the crop can be harvested. In some varieties especially, the dying

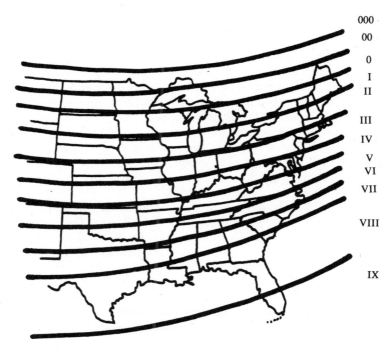

The northern-most twelve maturity groups in North America. Group X is adapted to the tropics.

plants tend to lodge, making harvesting difficult, and in some varieties, pods tend to split open (shatter), dropping the seed and reducing harvestable yield.

As soybean seeds lose moisture they change from large, kidney bean shaped to smaller and nearly round. When dry, the seed contains about 40% protein, 21% oil, 34% carbohydrates and 5% ash.

Varieties. There is an amazing number of soybean varieties. Just about every valley in China, Japan and Korea grows its own variety, adapted to local conditions. A collection of over 10,000 strains of soybean seeds is maintained by the USDA. A glance of an assortment of these seeds reveals seeds of every color and description—some red, some green, some black, some brown, some speckled or streaked, some large and some tiny.

The great majority of soybean varieties grown commercially today is for animal feed and oil production (for food processing and industrial uses). Most are yellow-seeded field varieties. Other varieties can be obtained for special uses: forage and hay (with an abundance of stems and leaves; small-seeded black and brown late varieties) and human food (large-seeded, various-colored varieties). For the most part, we will stick to commercial field varieties in this book, except for the last chapter.

Hybrids. Commercial hybrid soybean seed is very difficult to produce. This is because of the way the soybean reproduces: it is self-pollinating. Hybrids are made by soybean seed breeders, but it is a laborious, expensive process. From various ancestral and hybrid varieties, the commercial varieties are developed, both by agricultural experiment stations and private seed companies.

Seed quality. Varieties are developed to produce high yields of good quality seed, to mature properly for the geographic area, to be resistant to lodging and shattering, to be cold and drought tolerant, and to resist diseases and pests. Factors of seed quality may include low numbers of defective or shriveled seeds, high germination rate, high oil and/or protein content and human food value.

Soybean seeds sold by reliable seed dealers should come with certain important information: the variety, the Maturity Group number, percent inert matter, percent weed seed, percent other crop seed, germination rate and resistance to diseases and/or pests. The U.S. plant variety protection act of 1970 and the earlier federal seed act, as well as state seed laws, provide standards and protection to dealers, but some private growers may not adhere to these standards. Anyone can save some of his seed to grow the next year, but this is no assurance of quality.

Selecting a variety. In selecting which variety you wish to plant, assuming you are growing field soybeans, you need to consider several things. First, buy the best quality seed you can find. Certified tested seed is usually worth the cost. You can test for germination rate by counting out 25 whole seeds and roll them up in a damp cloth. Keep in a warm (70 to 80 degrees F.) place. Sprinkle with water if necessary to keep the cloth moist. After five or six days, unroll the cloth and count the seeds that have germinated out of 25. Multiply by 4 and divide by 100 to get the percentage germination.

Be sure to get seed of a Maturity Group adapted to your area. You may want to vary slightly the maturity group depending on soil type (an early variety for cool, wet, fine-textured soils and a later variety on coarse, well-drained soils). Avoid early varieties in fields where tall broadleaf weeds may get out of hand. If you want to follow the soybeans with fall-seeded small grains, use an early-maturing soybean.

One way to allow for uncertain weather conditions is to plant more than one maturity, either in different fields or as a seed blend, a mixture of varieties. That way at least one variety should give a reasonably good yield. If you save your own seed to replant, you will not get the same proportion as what was in the blend.

Select a variety that is shatter and lodging resistant, expecially if you intend to plant high populations, since the plants will grow taller, more slender stems.

Disease and insect resistance may be important if these have been a problem in your area; however, by improving your soil's fertility and structure, most such problems should disappear (see Chap. 3).

Indeterminate varieties should be used in the North, and determinate varieties do not do well in soils that crust. For wide rows, bushy varieties are best, to fill in the space quickly.

If you use a grain drill for planting, avoid seed lots with many large seeds, which do not flow well through the drill. Use seed lots with 2,400 seeds per pound or less. Small-seeded varieties have some advantages: the seedlings emerge better through crusted soil, fewer pounds of seed are needed to establish a certain plant population, and it is often easier to produce high quality grain (because smaller seeds suffer less damage during harvesting and handling).

You can often get valuable advice on selecting varieties from your agricultural research and extension personnel or from seed dealers. They may have performance test results which can be a rough guide of what to expect from a variety.

CHAPTER 2

Getting Started

The first thing we need to think about before doing any field work is the soil and its fertility, for without good soil it is impossible to grow a good crop. And a good soil will actually give the plants protection from adverse weather—cold, frost, drought, excess water—as well as protection from pests and diseases.

Fortunately, the soybean is a hardy, not-too-particular plant and can do reasonably well in a variety of soils and soil conditions, but to produce high yields of top quality soybeans, you need to get your soil into really good condition.

The ideal soil. Ideal soil for peak soybean production is a loose, well-drained loam. All too many fields these days have tight, crusty soil that becomes waterlogged when it rains. More than likely, such soil is low in humus and has an imbalance in mineral nutrients. Probably there are few beneficial soil organisms (certain bacteria, fungi, algae, protozoa, earthworms and others). In short, the soil is "dead."

The advantages of loose, well-aerated soil with adequate humus and abundant living organisms include the following: (1) Loose, aerated soil allows air to get to roots and nitrogen-fixing root nodules, plus it soaks up rain and lessens erosion, and it discourages many of the worst weeds. (2) Humus and soil organisms provide steady, balanced nutrition to roots, soak up and hold moisture (provide "drought-proofing"), and protect roots from harmful nematodes, insects and disease pathogens. (3) Organic matter also tends to buffer soil from extremes in pH (acidity and alkalinity).

Modern agriculture. Yet many of today's agricultural practices tend to degrade soil and produce the tight, crusty, lifeless conditions mentioned earlier. The overuse of synthetic salt fertilizers and anhydrous ammonia tends to reduce soil life and humus, leading to hard soil. Some of the herbicides and pesticides also do the same thing. Too much field traffic and heavy machinery compact soil. Even using the wrong kind of lime may in some cases lead to soil degradation.

Soil Air

Loose, well-aerated soil is extremely important in growing healthy, high-producing crops. In the classic text, *Soil Conditions and Plant Growth* (by E.J. & E.W. Russell, 8th ed., p. 335), we read:

> The soil pores that are not filled with water contain gases . . . the rate of transfer of carbon dioxide from the root zone to the atmosphere and of oxygen from the atmosphere to the root zone is a soil property of fundamental importance to the crop, and in humid soils the rate of oxygen penetration probably limits root growth more often than the rate of carbon dioxide removal; the oxygen supply is as important in humid soils as is the water supply in arid.

Low oxygen and high carbon dioxide in the soil's pores can cause a multitude of problems, ranging from damaged roots to toxins released from harmful soil organisms to loss of soil nitrogen to insect attack to low crop yield and poor quality. More details are given in *The Coming Revolution in Agriculture*, Chapter 3.

How can soil be kept loose and well-aerated? The best long-term solution is to maintain adequate levels of organic matter and to foster beneficial soil life, including earthworms, whose burrows add greatly to soil aeration (see *The Rest of the Story*, p. 62.

Organic matter makes soil loose and holds water. It is also a food supply for the beneficial soil organisms. The microscopic soil organisms, including bacteria and fungi, also help loosen soil because their by-products, sticky materials called polysaccharides, glue tiny soil particles together to form larger clumps called crumbs or aggregates.

Ways of increasing soil organic matter and improving the soil's crumb structure include incorporating animal manure (or better, rotted manure or compost) and plowing under a green manure crop. Leaving a surface cover of plant residue also helps by reducing erosion and keeping soil moist (as long as it is not wet, waterlogged soil). The application of lime along with manure or other organic matter hastens the process of soil loosening. Leaving a field fallow with a cover crop of grasses and/or legumes will also greatly improve soil structure and fertility.

Nutrient needs. Plants need various amounts of nutrient elements from the soil as they grow and produce seeds. Other than nitrogen, they should be present in adequate amounts in ideal soils, but most soils either have deficiencies or imbalances in the amounts of nutrients available to the plants. Here is a brief summary of the soil nutrients:

Nitrogen. Nitrogen (abbreviated N) is needed by the plant for certain enzyme functions, to make proteins, and as a necessary part of chlorophyll, nucleic acids, vitamins and several other substances. Soybeans can obtain all the nitrogen they need from root nodule nitrogen-fixing bacteria. In fact, in tests where fertilizer nitrogen was added to soil, no yield increase occurred, plus the root nodules fixed less nitrogen.

You should need to add no nitrogen fertilizer when growing soybeans unless root nodules do not form well, which can happen the first time soybeans are grown in a field or when soil conditions are toxic to the nodule

---

Diseased Soil?

The pioneer of composting, Sir Albert Howard, calls *erosion* a soil disease in his book, *The Soil and Health*, p. 85: "Perhaps the most widespread and most important disease of the soil at the present time is soil erosion . . ."

He states that the keys to the solution of soil erosion are humus and soil microbes, p. 86: "The fragments of mineral matter derived form the weathering of rocks [soil particles] are combined by means of the specks of glue-like organic matter supplied mostly by the dead bodies of the soil bacteria which live on humus . . .

"Provided, however, that we keep up the bacterial population of the land . . . the supplies of glue for making new compound soil particles [soil aggregates] and for repairing the old ones will be assured.

"It will be seen from this how fundamentally important is the role of humus. It is the humus which feeds the bacterial life, which, so to say, glues the soil together and makes it effective."

Howard calls soil erosion a "man-made disease" and says that it is *"always preceded by infertility"* (p. 87). He then places the blame: "Soil erosion is nothing less than the outward and visible sign of the complete failure of a farming policy. The root causes of this failure are to be found in ourselves."

Sick soil does not have to be a casualty. The patient can recover if the principles of eco-agriculture are applied.

bacteria. From 60 to 80 pounds per acre of supplemental nitrogen can then be applied between one month after emergence and first flowering.

Phosphorus (P). Soybeans need a lot of phosphorus, which is used for general growth and metabolism and for photosynthesis. It carries energy from one part of a cell to another and helps transport food from one part of the plant to another. It also makes up part of cell membranes, nucleic acids and other components. It is necessary for growing really high quality crops. Young seedlings especially need available phosphorus.

The soil has plenty of phosphorus, but most of it is tied up in insoluble soil minerals and in soil organic matter. The best way to get phosphorus to crop plants is to have soil with adequate levels of humus and beneficial soil organisms, which decompose organic matter and break down soil minerals to release nutrients to the plants.

Adding soluble phosphorus fertilizers (superphosphate, triple superphosphate, etc.) does little good because these soluble forms quickly change back to insoluble mineral phosphate. Good sources of soil-building natural phosphate fertilizers are soft rock (colloidal) phosphate and basic slag. These contain a small proportion of available phosphorus, plus some calcium and trace elements.

Potassium (K). Needed for the plant's enzyme functions, food transport, protein and chlorophyll production, and in regulating water balance, potassium is needed by soybeans in fairly large amounts.

As with phosphorus, most soils (except sand) contain large amounts of potassium, but mostly tied up in the minerals of the soil. If soil organisms are healthy and active, the crop plants should receive enough potassium, since soil microbes break it down from minerals.

If your soil is very low in potassium, the best overall fertilizer source is potassium sulfate (0-0-50). Avoid using potassium chloride (0-0-60, muriate of potash), since it has a high salt index, and the chloride ion can injure soil microbes as well as soybeans themselves if present in high amounts. Potassium sulfate is more expensive than potassium chloride, but only about one-half as much is needed, and the extra sulfur is usually beneficial.

Calcium (Ca). Adequate available calcium levels are very important in growing high quality soybeans. Calcium is vitally important for cell division, root hair growth, enzyme functions and normal cell walls. Calcium improves plants' resistance to disease and gives higher quality, more nutritious crops.

Calcium and **magnesium** (Mg) are connected in plant useage. Magnesium is needed as part of chlorophyll and in nucleic acids, cell membranes and protein-producing structures. In the soil, calcium and magnesium "compete" for plant absorption. Too much magnesium upsets the plant's use of calcium and potassium, giving rise to low quality crops, plus in some soils, excess magnesium leads to hard, crusty conditions. Most soils (except acid, sandy soils) should have plenty of magnesium, so none should be added. In general, soils in the western two-thirds of the U.S. have adequate calcium, while those in the eastern one-third may be deficient.

The best way to add calcium to soils is to use high-calcium lime (calcium carbonate). It has little magnesium and dissolves fairly quickly (moreso if finely ground). The use of dolomitic lime (calcium magnesium carbonate) is unnecessary if soil already has enough magnesium, plus dolomitic lime is hard and slow to dissolve. In alkaline soil, gypsum (calcium sulfate) is the best calcium source.

Sulfur (S). Soybeans use quite a lot of sulfur, which is needed to build proteins and in enzyme functions. Many soils have adequate sulfur because of air pollution from burning high-sulfur coal, but other soils are deficient.

If sulfur is needed, use sulfate-containing fertilizers (calcium sulfate, potassium sulfate), not elemental sulfur (flowers of sulfur), which is slow to become available.

Micronutrients. Other elements are needed by plants, but only in very small amounts. Thus they are called the micronutrients or trace elements. Important are *iron* (Fe), *zinc* (Zn), *copper* (Cu), *boron* (B), *manganese* (Mn), *molybdenum* (Mo), *cobalt* (Co) and *chlorine* (Cl).

In soybeans, the most frequent micronutrient deficiencies are for iron, zinc, manganese and molybdenum. But such deficiencies usually occur in poor, weathered or sandy soils, or in soils that are very alkaline or excessively high in organic matter (mucks and peats). A loamy soil with adequate humus and soil life should not have micronutrient deficiencies.

If a micronutrient is deficient in your soil, add only that element, not a "shotgun" trace element fertilizer, since too much of some micronutrients will be toxic.

Balance. For healthy crops and high quality yields, it is important that nutrient elements be available to the plants in the proper amounts and in the right balance. Too much or too little of some elements can cause deficiencies of others.

pH. The acidity or alkalinity of the soil is called pH. It is expressed on a numerical scale ranging from 0 (most acid) to 14 (most alkaline), with 7 being neutral. Soybeans can tolerate a wide range of pH if they have adequate nutrients, but do best in slightly acid soil, from pH 5.8 to 7.0.

Soil pH affects the availability of nutrient elements and the types and ability of soil organisms to live, including nitrogen-fixing bacteria. Extremely-acid (low pH) or alkaline (high pH) conditions are bad, but in normal fertile soil, pH can fluctuate over a growing season without harm. Adequate humus levels in soil will buffer extremes in pH and bring soil toward best pH levels.

Lime has been used to counteract soil acidity and raise pH, but its primary value is adding calcium. A healthy, humus-rich soil is the best insurance against extreme pH.

Soil tests. In order to get your soil into a proper balance of nutrients, you should have fequent soil tests made (at least once or twice a year, in spring and fall). The trouble with soil tests is that some are more reliable than others, and there are various ways of testing soil, some of which give accurate results but tell you little about what your crops really need. The type of soil test which gives the most useful information is a water-soluble test. This test tells how much nutrient is available to the plant at that time, rather than the total nutrients in the soil (but mostly unavailable). Most testing labs do not run water-soluble tests unless you request them.

Tests may vary slightly, but using one method (the LaMotte system), desirable water-soluble levels for major nutrients are:

> 2000 pounds/acre *calcium*
> 400 pounds/acre *phosphate* (P_2O_5)
> 200 pounds/acre *potassium*
> 40 pounds/acre *nitrogen*

These figures do not translate to non-water-soluble tests and may be higher or lower than most experts recommend, but they do produce high quality crops. Generally, one should not worry about trace elements until the major elements are at proper levels.

Plant tissue testing, as done by most labs, is not as informative as water soluble soil tests. Tissue tests only test the soluble contents of the cells. Some nutrients are part of the cell structure and are not soluble. Sometimes the soil may have plenty of nutrients, but they are not getting into the plant because of poor root functions or toxic soil conditions.

Tillage. Tillage is done for three reasons: to prepare a seedbed or improve soil structure, to incorporate organic matter and fertilizers, and to control weeds. There are several commonly used tillage methods. The moldboard plow lifts and turns the soil, inverting the plow layer. This causes drastic disturbance in the soil ecosystem, but can be useful in heavy soils if done in the fall. Winter freezing and thawing may improve soil structure.

Chisel plows fracture the soil rather than turning it. Less energy is needed to pull the plow, and the soil is disturbed less. Some plant residue is left on the surface, which is helpful for reducing erosion.

Discs cut and loosen soil and incorporate much of the plant residue, but they compact the soil beneath the blades.

Field cultivators and springtooth harrows dig and lift the upper layers of soil and do not compact lower soil. Little residue is incorporated.

Rotary hoes break up clods and crusts and leave a fine-particle layer.

Subsoilers and deep chisels are used to fracture subsoil and break up hardpans, in an attempt to improve drainage and deep soil structure. Generally the effects are temporary, and without increasing soil humus, hard soil conditions will return.

In general, tillage on humus-poor, heavy soils causes deleterious effects, especially if overdone. Soil structure is destroyed, organic matter disappears and erosion increases. Tillage operations should be kept to a minimum if soil is poor.

No-till. The above disadvantages of tillage in poor soils have led to the development and promotion of various reduced- and no-till systems. By using special planters that can operate in surface crop residue and by using high levels of herbicide for weed control, crops can be grown fairly successfully (except in northern climates on poorly drained clay soils).

While it is true that reduced-tillage systems do reduce erosion and save fuel, the requirements for high amounts of fertilizer and pesticides and the long-term tendency for deep soil to become depleted in oxygen and toxic are disadvantages. Soil-living pests and diseases often increase, and springtime soil temperatures may be cold.

All of these disadvantages of no-till could be eliminated and most of the advantages obtained if an adequate level of humus (up to 10 to 12%) is maintained in the soil and if the use of materials toxic to soil organisms is reduced or eliminated (pesticides, some herbicides, high-salt and chlorine-containing fertilizers, over-use of raw manure). Humus and soil life create loose, non-crusting soil structure and break up hard subsoil and hardpans, improving drainage. Erosion is greatly reduced because humus holds soil particles in small clumps (aggregates).

Ridge planting. A fairly new tillage method that works well in some cases for corn and soybeans is called ridge planting or ridge-till. Rows must be at least 30 inches apart to allow ridges and valleys to be built up (branching varieties of soybeans must be used). The crop is planted on top of the ridges, with crop residue left in the valleys. Earlier planting is possible because ridge tops warm up soon, and wind erosion is reduced. Ridges catch more snow in winter. Weeds can be cultivated out in the valleys and if necessary, in-row herbicide can be used. Ridges must be built up each year, and machinery must be compatible with the ridge widths.

Which? The tillage methods you use should depend on your climate, soil type, slope, crop rotation, machinery and costs.

Cropping systems. Most people grow soybeans in a crop rotation sequence, typically with a non-legume such as corn, small grains, sorghum or cotton. The yield of the non-legume is improved because of the left-over nitrogen from the soybean root nodules. Also, disease, pest and weed problems are reduced in rotations compared to growing one crop continuously. These disadvantages can be overcome if soil is in peak fertility and condition.

Soybeans are also often grown in a double-cropping system, with two crops being grown in the same year. Winter wheat followed by soybeans is the most common; snapbeans or peas followed by soybeans is another. Timing is critical in more northerly areas.

Intercropping, in which two crops are planted in alternating rows or strips, or in which one crop is broadcast into the other, has been tried with mixed success. Sometimes aerial seeding was used. Conditions must be just right. Examples include planting soybeans in standing small grain, small grain into growing soybeans, ryegrass or clover into growing soybeans, alternate strips of corn and soybeans, corn and soybeans in the same rows, and early soybeans into a growing late variety. Interseeding grasses or legume-grass mixtures into soybeans at the leaf-yellow or leaf-drop stage will provide an excellent erosion reducing ground cover over the winter that can be worked into the soil next spring.

Row width. In northern and central regions of the U.S., soybeans grown in narrow rows yield more than those grown in corn-width rows. In southern areas, the same may be true if good weed control is achieved. To produce maximum yield, soybean foliage should completely cover the space between rows by the time flowering begins. The plants tend to do this anyway, producing more branches in wide rows (but if you use wide rows, be sure to plant a bushy variety). The faster the foliage covers the ground, the less weeds are a problem, but one cannot cultivate weeds with narrow rows.

In recent years row widths have decreased, averaging about 18 inches and sometimes as small as 7 inches (and experimentally even 2½ inches). Newer planters will plant narrow rows, or older planters can often be modified. It is recommended that soil fertility for narrow rows be increased 10 to 20% over levels for wide rows.

Population. Soybeans can adjust to a wide range of plant populations. Yields remain fairly constant within a range of 70,000 to 180,000 plants per acre. For wide rows, about 150,000 is a good target, with 175,000 for narrow rows (solid seeding). At lower populations, plants branch more and lodge less, while at high populations the opposite is true. Pods form higher on the plant in high populations. Weeds are more of a problem in low populations, Populations should be adjusted to reduce lodging and keep pods high on the plant. Populations can be increased when growing determinate, semi-dwarf and non-branching varieties.

Seedbed preparation. An ideal seedbed for soybeans should provide adequate moisture and warmth for rapid germination and seedling establishment. Soil should be friable and not crusted. Germination of weed seeds should be delayed or prevented.

Soybeans need a lot of moisture to germinate (50% of their weight). Soil moisture must be sufficient at planting depth. There should be good soil-seed contact. If soybeans get off to a rapid start, young weeds can be shaded out. One way to discourage weeds is to prepare an ideal seedbed only in the rows and leave the soil rough and cloddy or covered by residue between the rows. Another approach is to prepare the seedbed well ahead of planting, let the weeds germinate, then retill just before planting to kill sprouted weeds.

Most people use herbicides to control weeds, but such chemicals may have their deleterious environmental effects, and their use can be avoided as we shall see in the next chapter.

Planting. As mentioned earlier, use good quality seed of high germination rate (80 to 90% or more). If soybeans have not been grown on that soil for three to five years, it is best to inoculate the seed with the proper strain of nitrogen-fixing bacteria (*Rhizobium*). Some strains are more effective nitrogen fixers than others. The bacterial inoculant can be applied to the seed just before planting time or in the row during planting (the latter requires more inoculant).

Seed can also be treated with fungicide, but unless the soil is cold, if the germination rate is over 85%, there is little advantage in this. Lower germination seed may have a 5 to 10% increase in emergence if treated.

Early planting usually gives higher yields, but only if a good stand is obtained. Cool weather will delay germination and allow root diseases or pests to get a start. Soil and air temperatures of 55 to 60 degrees F. are needed for good germination and seedling establishment. Germination rates increase at warmer temperatures, and high quality seed is more likely to produce a good stand. The predicted weather is probably the most important factor to consider, along with your local soil conditions. Adequate moisture is essential for germination.

Planting rate. To achieve a desired population, you need to calculate the number of seeds required. Some seeds will not germinate, and some that germinate will not become established because of weather, pests or disease. Generally, if the seedbed and planter are good, about 90 to 95% of germinated seedlings will become established. To figure planting rate, use this formula:

$$\frac{\text{desired population per foot of row}}{\% \text{ germination X } \% \text{ expected establishment}} = \text{seeds needed per foot of row}$$

For example: $\dfrac{6}{.80 \text{ X } .95} = 7.9$ per foot of row

You need to plant 7.9 seeds per foot of row to get six plants per foot. Since soybean seed is usually sold by weight rather than by number of seeds, you need to know the number of seeds per pound to figure pounds needed per acre. If the seed dealer cannot give you number of seeds per pound, weigh a few one-ounce samples on a postage scale to get an average figure.

The number of linear feet of row per acre can be found from the accompanying table. Then figure the pounds of seed needed per acre:

$$\frac{\text{seeds per foot of row X total feet of row}}{\text{seeds per pound}} = \text{pounds of seed per acre}$$

For example: $\dfrac{7.9 \text{ X } 29,040}{3,500} = 65.5$ pounds of seed

Calibrate your planter accordingly and check seed drop in the field regularly.

Planting depth. Seeds should be planted deep enough to absorb enough moisture to germinate, but not so deep that they have trouble emerging from the soil. Some varieties can emerge from greater depths than others. Typical planting depths are 1 to 1½ inches, but if soil is low in moisture or sandy, plant 2 inches deep. In cool, moist soil seed can be planted 1 inch deep if there is no danger from herbicides.

Planting method. Best results are obtained using a unit planter or grain drill to plant in rows. Drills usually do not handle rough seedbeds as well as planters. Broadcasting or aerial seeding followed by light tillage to cover seed often results in uneven emergence and stands that are too thin in some areas and too thick in others.

Replanting. If a stand of soybeans is reduced by disease, pests, hail, flooding, herbicide injury, etc., replanting may be considered. If the loss is covered by crop insurance, consult your insurance agent first. If most of a field is lost, be sure enough growing season is left for beans to mature.

If the surviving population is 75% or more of the desired population, replanting is not necessary (unless weeds will be a problem) since the surviving plants will branch out to fill in gaps.

When replanting, you may want to use shallow tillage to kill young weeds. Do not apply herbicide. Use a variety with maturity date appropriate for the later planting date, increase the seeding rate by 10 to 15% and plant in narrow rows to increase yield.

LINEAR FEET PER ACRE AT DIFFERENT ROW WIDTHS	
(from *Modern Soybean Production*, 1983, p. 90)	
Row width in inches	**Linear feet of row per acre**
40	13,068
38	13,756
36	14,520
34	15,374
32	16,345
30	17,424
28	18,668
26	20,105
24	21,780
22	23,760
20	26,136
18	29,040
16	32,670
14	37,337
12	43,560
10	52,272
8	65,340
7	74,674
6	87,120

Above all, rely on the eco-principles set forth in *The Rest of the Story*, *The Coming Revolution in Agriculture*, and in *An Acres U.S.A. Primer* under topics such as soil, air, water and decay management.

CHAPTER 3

Problems

Agriculture tends to be full of unpleasant surprises. Things seldom seem to go right. The weather doesn't cooperate—too wet, too dry, too hot, too cold. Weeds, pests, diseases, all proliferate.

Most of these problems seem beyond the farmer's control, but there are things you can do to largely prevent or overcome most of the things that go wrong.

Emergence. The first problem likely to strike soybeans is difficulty for the seedling to break through a surface crust. This is an emergency, and you should break the crust immediately with a rotary hoe or cultivator. Driving on emerging soybeans will not significantly reduce stands.

The problem can be prevented by getting good soil structure so that crusting will not occur. This can be done by adding compost or light amounts of manure or poultry litter to the soil; that is, increase the soil's organic matter content. The organic matter should be worked into the upper several inches of soil.

Weeds. Weeds compete with soybeans for moisture, soil nutrients and sunlight, reducing yield. They can also interfere with harvesting, and their seeds contaminate harvested soybean seed. Weeds should be controlled if the probable yield loss (dollar loss) exceeds the cost of control.

Weeds can be controlled by management, mechanical and chemical control. Chemical control is rapidly becoming less an option. Heads-up biofarmers feel themselves secure in the knowledge that weed control is based on fertility management, and not in buying a more powerful poison from Dow Chemical or Monsanto. For weeds that have gesrminated, control must be made within the first four weeks after soybean emergence to prevent yield reduction. Weeds that emerge after six weeks will have little effect on yield.

Weeds growing before planting should be killed by seedbed preparation tillage. Soybean seeds should have good soil-seed contact to get the seedlings off to a rapid start so that the soybean foliage will shade out weeds. Deep-planted seedlings grow more slowly than shallow-planted ones. Leaving a rough between-row seedbed will slow down weeds. Narrow rows allow soybeans to shade out weeds more quickly.

Before soybeans are one inch high, rotary hoeing is an effective method of killing emerging weeds. It works best at relatively high speeds (8 to 12 miles per hour) late in the day when soybean seedlings are less brittle. A shovel cultivator is effective on small or larger weeds when soybean seedlings are a little larger. Shovels should be set at a shallow depth (1 to 2 inches) to reduce pruning of soybean roots. A rolling cultivator can also be used effectively for small weeds when operated at 6 to 10 miles per hour. These mechanical methods cannot be used in narrow-row or solid seeded stands.

The use of herbicides to control weeds in soybeans has grown gradually since World War II, and is now both questioned and under fire. Newer, more powerful herbicides have been developed. Some kill broadleaf weeds, others grasses. Some are applied before planting, others after soybean emergence. Some are incorporated into the soil, others are surface-applied. Some are more toxic than others, but they are all designed to kill living plants and thus should be used with great care if used at all. The *Acres U.S.A.* position is that they do not belong in a sound management program. Many problems can arise, including killing (or damaging) soybean seedlings, spray drift into unwanted areas, carryover into succeeding years, toxicity to beneficial soil organisms, and human or animal toxicity. Since most weeds can be eliminated by having healthy, balanced soil, herbicide use should be unnecessary.

Most of the weeds afflicting soybean growers prefer to grow in poor, out-of-balance, waterlogged or poorly aerated soil. These include quackgrass, giant foxtail, Johnsongrass, smartweed, bindweed and velvetleaf. I know it will be hard for some to believe, but the above weeds, and many others, grow best in "sick" soil; in healthy, balanced, well aerated soil, they grow poorly or not at all. A 2:1 phosphate to potassium ratio (as shown on water-soluble soil tests) will help eliminate weeds. Only a few weeds grow well on good soil. These include lamb's quarters and redroot (rough) pigweed. Milkweed, purselane and cocklebur grow well on fairly good soil.

Diseases. About 50 diseases attack soybeans in the U.S. with viruses, bacteria, fungi and nematodes (roundworms) being involved as pathogens. There are seed and seedling diseases, root diseases, stem and leaf diseases. Some can cause serious yield or quality losses, whereas others cause little problem. The worst are the fungal Phytophthora rot and the root knot nematode. Some varieties are resistant to these two diseases.

The thing about diseases is that they only attack plants that are already under stress. That is what really causes the disease. The so-called pathogens—bacteria, fungi, worms—then move in to destroy the sick and unfit plant. Nonsensically, we treat the symptoms and spray toxic chemicals to kill the pathogens and save the sick, poor quality crop. (Unfortunately farmers feel they have to do this to survive in farming today.)

The simple solution to crop diseases is this: healthy, vigorous plants growing in good, balanced soil don't get sick. They have the ability to resist disease pathogens in much the same way as our bodies resist germs, as long as we eat right, get plenty of rest and exercise, and avoid stress. Plants often resist diseases by producing substances that prevent pathogens from growing; some of these are called phytoalexins.

Of course, the way to grow healthy plants is to have fertile soil with good structure. As we have mentioned earlier, this means well aerated, loose soil with high levels of humus and beneficial soil organisms, and high, balanced levels of nutrients (high calcium is essential for disease resistance, for example). Some of the beneficial soil organisms actually protect a plant's roots from pathogenic bacteria, fungi and nematodes. Others channel nutrients and water into the roots, helping the plant to grow.

If your soil is in good shape, the only other stresses that could affect the plant are from adverse weather. But even here, good soil can counteract most weather stresses. Loose, well drained soil will soak up heavy rain. Humus holds water in drought conditions, and the sticky secretions of soil microbes also help drought-proof soil. Friable soil will not crust and will allow plenty of air to reach roots and nitrogen-fixing bacteria. Most disease pathogens cannot live in well-aerated soil.

Pests. The story about soybean pests is about the same as for diseases and weeds. Many species of insects and mites will attack soybeans, although only a few cause economically serious damage. Some eat seeds and roots, others attack stems, leaves or pods. Some chew, while others suck juices. Again, the scientists come to the rescue by spraying toxic chemicals (and a farmer may feel he has to resort to that technology to save a crop), but again, the simple solution is the same—healthy, vigorous plants growing in good soil. Such plants are naturally immune or resistant to pest attack. The pests either avoid the plant altogether or else just take a few nibbles and then go away.

As with herbicides, toxic fungicides, insecticides, and other pesticides, their use should become unnecessary after ecological farming principles have been used for a year or two.

Nutrient deficiencies. If a plant is not getting the proper amounts of nutrient elements, it may develop certain symptoms, abnormal colors or growth deformities. By the time these symptoms appear, it is often too late to do much to alleviate the problem (unless plants are still small or you can foliar feed them), but you can try to trace the cause and overcome it for the future.

Nutrient deficiency symptoms may not necessarily mean one or more elements are deficient in the soil. The nutrient may be adequate but the plant may not be able to take it up, perhaps because of high or low pH, or too much or too little of some other soil element. Or perhaps stress on the plant from drought, wet soil, cold weather or toxic soil conditions causes roots not to absorb the element. Nutrient deficiency symptoms in soybeans are listed in the accompanying box.

MINERAL DEFICIENCY SYMPTOMS IN SOYBEANS
(from *Modern Soybean Production*, 1983, p. 171-73)

- *Nitrogen.* Pale green or yellowish leaves. Seldom a problem if root nodule bacteria are present. Can be due to a molybdenum deficiency.
- *Phosphorus.* Plants stunted; leaves blue-green and sometimes cupped
- *Potassium.* Irregular yellow border around leaves.
- *Calcium.* Few nitrogen-fixing root nodules, causing nitrogen deficiency symptoms.
- *Magnesium.* Leaves turning yellow or brown between veins; leaf tip curled down.
- *Sulfur.* Slow growth; leaves becoming yellowish.
- *Iron.* Slow growth; new leaves yellow or brown between veins.
- *Manganese.* Leaves light green to white between veins.
- *Molybdenum.* Reduced growth; leaves with nitrogen deficiency symptoms.
- *Zinc.* Plants stunted; lower leaves turning yellow to brown to gray and dropping off; young plants with pale green leaves. Few flowers and pods; pods mature slowly.

Sick root nodules. Healthy, active nitrogen-fixing root nodules will have a pink or reddish internal color. You should monitor the health of these furnishers of free nitrogen by occasionally digging up a plant and examining its root nodules. They should be abundant and pink when cut open (until the plant begins its period of senescence; see Chap.1). If the nodules are few in number or greenish or yellowish inside, something is wrong in the soil. Perhaps there are toxic substances (from pesticides or too much raw organic matter) in the soil which are harming the bacteria. Perhaps the soil is poorly aerated, since nitrogen-fixing bacteria need oxygen and nitrogen from the air. Perhaps there is a molybdenum deficiency or low pH (acid). Perhaps the soil already has plenty of nitrogen, either from past fertilizers or from heavy manure application (this is not necessarily a problem, however). Sick root nodules are just one more symptom that you may be able to use to trace down and solve a problem.

Foliar feeding. If your soybeans seem to be lagging in growth or standing still, perhaps because of weather stress (cool, cloudy weather), you may be able to give them a "shot in the arm" and pull them out of it. With a high value crop such as soybeans, it may be economically feasible to foliar feed to help the plants along.

Foliar feeding is a complex subject that cannot be covered thoroughly here, but in general it allows you to supply small amounts of deficient elements to plants (through their leaves, primarily) at the time they need them. Fertilizers applied to the soil before planting may not be available to the plants when they need them most—during peak growth and pod fill. Foliar spraying is not an effective way to deliver large amounts of major nutrients (so it is best to have them in your soil already), but it can help pull your crop through a difficult period and produce a good yield. Foliar spraying will often stimulate the plant to take up more of the soil's nutrients.

Ordinary field sprayers do not produce a very fine spray, so they waste a lot of material. Better sprayers homogenize or atomize the spray, allowing you to spray a field for only cents per acre in some cases. You can mix your own tailor-made spray mixture with a little experience, depending on what your plants need at that time.

A good "all-purpose" spray is a mixture of about 6 quarts liquid (emulsified) fish and 2 quarts seaweed, diluted in 100 gallons of water (deionized or soft water is best). The fish and seaweed mixture should be acid (pH 5-6.5); this can be done by first adding from 1 pint to 2 quarts of liquid-phosphoric acid to the 100 gallons of water. The liquid fish should be strained to keep from plugging your sprayer. Spray at the rate of 1 quart of the mixture per acre if you have a homogenizing sprayer, or until plants are wet.

Another spray mixture for young soybeans when soil fertility is low (low calcium and phosphorus, especially) is as follows: add in this order to 100 gallons water, (1) up to 2 gallons of 9% ammonia solution (or household ammonia); (2) up to 2 quarts liquid phosphoric acid (available from feed dealers or pharmacies); (3) 1-2 pounds of iron sulfate (dissolve first in warm water); (4) 5 pounds of soft rock phosphate (stir into a container of water and skim off and use the white, milky water above the mineral); and (5) 1 pound potassium sulfate (or 8 ounces potassium hydroxide). Spray at a rate of 7 gallons per acre, or until plants are wet.

If older soybeans have blossoms falling off and failing to set seeds (some will do this anyway), a spray mixture that may help contains, in 100 gallons of water: (1) up to 2 quarts liquid phosphoric acid; (2) 1-2 gallons ammonia solution; (3) 1-2 pounds iron sulfate (dissolve first in warm water); (4) up to 8 ounces manganese sulfate; (5) 5 pounds soft rock phosphate (stir into a container of water and use milky water); and (6) 1 quart emulsified oil (crop oil, dormant oil). Spray at 7 gallons per acre, or until plants are wet. Additional sprayings may be needed at one-week intervals; if so, use ingredients at one-half strength and eliminate the emulsified oil.

Even after soybeans are older and filling seeds, yield can sometimes be increased by using a fish emulsion spray (2 gallons fish per 100 gallons water; spray until plants are wet). Do not use fish sprays after two weeks before cutting if the crop is for hay or forage, since animals do not like the taste.

Many proprietary brands of biologicals suitable for spraying are now on the market, and are advertised in *Acres U.S.A.*

Researchers at Iowa State University developed a foliar spray mixture that increased yield substantially when sprayed after pod set, since at that time root nodules begin to die and disintegrate. Their spray contained nitrogen,

---

Spray with Hydrogen Peroxide

An interesting development on the eco-agriculture scene is the use of hydrogen peroxide, H_2O_2, in a variety of ways. When added to animals' drinking water in diluted amounts (about 30 parts hydrogen peroxide per one million parts water; or about 8-10 oz. of 35% hydrogen peroxide [or 3 quarts of 3% hydrogen peroxide] in 1000 gallons of water), the incidence of disease and sickness drops dramatically, from pneumonia to mastitis. Meat and milk production rise. Hydrogen peroxide solution can also be used to drench animals, as an udder wash, and to rinse dairy pipelines and bulk tanks. In animal (or human) use, it appears to act by providing more oxygen to internal tissues (hydrogen peroxide is basically water, H_2O, with an extra oxygen atom, H_2O_2). Externally it also acts as a disinfectant, killing germs.

But hydrogen peroxide also helps plants grow better, although the mechanism is not clear. If seeds are soaked in a hydrogen peroxide solution (1 to 5 oz. of 3% hydrogen peroxide in 1 pint water or ½ to 2 oz. of 35% hydrogen peroxide in 2 quarts water) for about 8 hours, the percent germination should increase (germinating seeds need oxygen).

For a foliar spray to perk up growing plants, use 1 pint of 35% hydrogen peroxide (or 11 pints of 3% hydrogen peroxide) in 20 gallons of water to spray one acre.

Hydrogen peroxide also makes an effective insect spray. Use at a rate of about ½ pint of 3% hydrogen peroxide (or 1 oz. of 35% hydrogen peroxide) along with ½ pint of molasses per gallon of water (equal to about 6 gallons of 3% hydrogen peroxide [or 5 pints of 35% hydrogen peroxide] and 6 gallons of molasses per 100 gallons water). The molasses helps the solution stick to the plants and also gums up small insects. What drips onto the ground will help the plants grow better, too.

The preferred form of hydrogen peroxide is 35%, or food grade. It is harder to get than the 3% solution sold in grocery and drug stores. The latter has small amounts of preservative chemicals added, but they may not be harmful when used on plants.

phosphorus, potassium and sulfur in the ratio 10:1:3:0.5. The fertilizer source materials they used were urea, a 3-20-18 formulation containing polyphosphate, and potassium sulfate or ammonium sulfate. Some sprays also contained 5% sugar. When tested by researchers in other states, results were disappointing, possibly because of soil imbalances. Most observers expected the Iowa State program to fail because it cost too much, and because the preparations were in danger of burning the plants.

Feeding foliar sprays through an irrigation system is an effective method of application if you are able to do this.

The best times to spray are in foggy weather or in the early morning (4:00 to 6:00 a.m.), since this is when the plants take in nutrients best. The evening (after 7:00 p.m.) is another good time to spray. Be certain your sprayer has no traces of herbicides or pesticides. Clean thoroughly with baking soda solution.

You can test to see whether the spray mixture is going to help your crop if you spray several plants with a small hand sprayer (such as used with window-cleaning products). Wait a half hour and then test the sugar content of sprayed plants with a refractometer (see next section) compared to unsprayed plants. If the sugar content increased, the mixture is beneficial.

Quality. A last potential problem in growing soybeans is plants that grow poorly or produce poor quality seed. Sometimes the reason is a low rate of photosynthesis, possibly due to cloudy, cool weather—or the opposite extreme, heat and drought. Nutrient deficiencies, covered earlier, may contribute. Unfavorable soil conditions—waterlogging and poor aeration—can also disrupt normal plant functions.

Healthy plants will produce more nutritious food and seeds with more protein and oil. High quality seed will have a higher test weight.

A handy tool to help you monitor the health of your growing plants is a refractometer. This is a precision instrument which quickly measures the percent sugars in a plant's sap, while you are standing in the field. In general, the higher the sugar content, the higher the protein and oil content, since sugars are later turned into protein and oil. Fairly inexpensive, refractometers are routinely used in the food industry, by canneries, wineries and breweries, for example, to measure the quality of the fruits and vegetables they buy from the farmer or of the foods and drinks they manufacture.

Using a refractometer is easy. Just squeeze a drop or two of juice from the stem or leaves of the plant onto the glass prism of the refractometer, close the "lid" and look through the eyepiece. The sugar content is read on a numbered scale in units called *brix* (same as percent).

By comparing with standard readings or with past readings you have made, you can see how your crops measure up that day. Be careful to always take a reading from the same part of a plant (upper mature leaves and stems are good) each time and at the same time of day. The sugar content will vary in different parts of the plant, at different times and in different weather con-

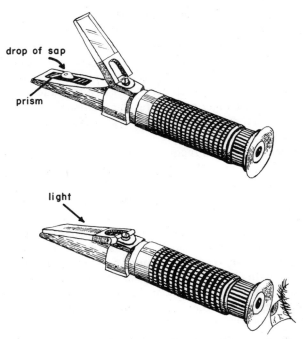

ditions (higher on warm, sunny days in the afternoon). Sometimes a sick plant will have a high sugar reading in the early morning, whereas a healthy plant should not.

STANDARD REFRACTOMETER READINGS FOR SOYBEANS & PEAS

Poor	Average	Good	Excellent
4	6	10	12

Find out what's wrong. You can't really tell what is going on in your fields while driving by at 50 miles per hour. You need to stop and walk through your fields and carefully *observe* what is happening. Look for telltale signs of insect damage or mineral deficiency in your plants. Check their sugar content with a refractometer. Are there isolated problem areas in a field?

Most important, check your soil. Carry a shovel and occasionally dig down and turn up a shovelfull of soil. Is it loose and friable, or tight and hard? Is there a hardpan six inches under? Are there earthworms, and fungi in last year's residues? Does the soil have that good rich smell of humus? Is there a weed problem?

Dig up the root system of a plant. Are the roots a healthy white color or discolored with decaying spots? Are there plenty of nitrogen-fixing nodules on the upper roots? Are the nodules a healthy pink inside?

These are all things you should notice and questions you should be able to answer about your fields. If you spot a problem, figure out its cause and work to overcome it. The basic place to begin is the soil.

CHAPTER 4

Harvesting and Storage

A t the end of the growing season comes the most important part of soybean production—harvesting.

The beans contain 45 to 55% moisture when mature (filled) and must dry
down before being harvested. When field mature, seeds, pods and stem turn
yellow. About four to nine days later, all pods on the plant have turned
brown. At this point, seed moisture is about 33%. With good drying
weather, the beans should be ready to harvest four to five days after this.
They should be at 13 to 14% moisture, but with careful combining, beans of
higher moisture can be successfully harvested. Shattering losses are very high
below 13% moisture.

Grain elevators or seed dealers will usually measure moisture content of
grain if you do not have your own meter. As a rough indication, a well dried
(13% moisture) soybean will split in two easily when tapped with a hammer.

Chemicals? If dry-down is not likely to occur rapidly, chemical desiccant
(drying) sprays can be used. Weeds are also killed at the same time. Early
harvested beans usually command a higher market price, and field losses are
lower with early harvest. But the desiccant kills the plant, and should not be
used before seed maturity has been reached or significant yield reduction will
occur. The chemicals used for drying include sodium chlorate, a powerful
oxidant, and the herbicide Paraquat. Many specialists question the practice
of using desiccants, and mention of the practice here does not constitute en-
dorsement.

Reduce losses. It is very important to keep harvesting losses to a minimum
in a high-value crop. Lodging and shattering losses can be partially reduced
by planting resistant varieties and appropriate populations. Shattering is
more likely the longer the plants stand in the field, especially with alternating
wet and dry weather.

It is extremely important that the combine be adjusted and operated properly. Keep the machine in good repair. Adjust reel speed to 25% faster than
ground speed. Six-bat reels feed more evenly than four- or five-bat reels.

Operate the cutterbar as close to the ground as possible. Use a pick-up reel with lodged soybeans. Generally ground speed should not exceed three miles per hour to prevent stripping of beans from the stalk; slower speeds are necessary if plant height is uneven.

Handling. Avoid excessive impact of harvested grain on hard surfaces, since dry soybeans crack easily. Run conveyors as full and as slowly as possible. Use cushion boxes to absorb impact from long drops. Warm up cold beans by aeration before transfer, since cold beans crack more easily.

Drying. Soybeans above 14% moisture should be dried. The same drying equipment used for other grains can be used for soybeans. At high drying temperatures (over 100 degrees F.) germination rate, oil and protein quality are harmed. In low humidity weather, no artificial heat may be necessary. If the outside humidity is below 70% and temperature above 60 degrees F., good drying will occur. A perforated floor under the grain gives better air distribution than ducts. An air flow of 2 to 3 cubic feet per minute is recommended.

To prevent seed coat cracking, drying air should be above 40% relative humidity. The relative humidity of air is approximately cut in half for every 20 degrees F. rise in temperature. Say the outside humidity is 100% at 50 degrees F. If you raise your drying air to 70 degrees F., its humidity will be 50% An additional rise to 90 degrees F. will bring the humidity too low, 25%, and many seeds will crack.

About 2,000 BTU of heat are needed to evaporate a pound of water. You

AMOUNT OF WATER IN A BUSHEL OF SOYBEANS AT VARIOUS MOISTURE CONTENTS (from *Harvesting and Drying Soybeans*, University of Wisconsin-Extension Publ. A2665)				
		Excess water in pounds dried to		
% moisture content	Pounds of water per bushel	13%	12%	11%
24	16.5	8.7	9.4	10.1
22	14.7	6.9	7.6	8.3
20	13.1	5.3	6.0	6.7
18	11.5	3.7	4.4	5.1
16	9.9	2.1	2.8	3.5
14	8.5	0.7	1.4	2.1
13	7.8	0	0.7	1.4
12	7.1		0	0.7
11	6.45			0
10	5.8			

can figure the cost and time for drying a batch of soybeans. Using the accompanying table, find the pounds of water per bushel you need to dry, and multiply by total bushels. For example, to dry beans with 16% moisture to 12%, 2.8 pounds of water per bushel must be removed. This times 2,000 BTU equals 5,600 BTU per bushel.

To figure drying time, the BTU per hour equals air flow (in cubic feet per minute) times temperature increase. For example, at an air flow of 2 cfm and a temperature increase of 15 degrees F., the heat input is 30 BTU per hour per bushel. Thus to dry our beans from 16 to 12% moisture, we would need:

$$\frac{5,600}{30} = 186.7 \text{ hours or } 7.8 \text{ days.}$$

If you know the drying time and the horsepower required (see accompanying table), you can figure cost at 1 kilowatt hour per horsepower times electricity

APPROXIMATE HORSEPOWER REQUIRMENT FOR DRYING SOYBEANS (adapted from *Modern Soybean Production*, 1983, p. 188)								
Depth of Grain	Up to 20 ft.		20 - 30 ft.		30 - 40 ft.		40 - 50 ft.	
Air Flow (cfm)	.2	3	2	3	2	3	2	3
Bushels								
2,000	1.0	1.5	1.7	2.5	3.3	5.0	3.3	5.0
3,000	1.7	2.5	3.3	5.0	4.0	6.0	5.0	7.5
6,000	3.3	5.0	5.0	7.5	6.7	10.0	10.0	15.0
10,000	5.0	7.5	6.7	10.0	10.0	15.0	15.0	22.5
20,000	10.0	15.0	15.0	22.5	20.0	30.0	30.0	45.0
30,000	15.0	22.5	20.0	30.0	30.0	45.0	40.0	60.0
40,000	20.0	30.0	30.0	45.0	40.0	60.0	60.0	90.0
60,000	30.0	45.0	40.0	60.0	60.0	90.0	100.0	150.0

cost per kilowatt hour. If a heat source other than the motor and fan is used, the electricity or LP cost must be added on.

Storage. Stored grain must be kept cool and dry to prevent mold and insects from attacking. Damaged grain is also a detriment; insects seldom feed on whole soybeans. Foreign matter is often a source of mold growth. Soybeans lose and gain moisture quickly, so it is important that storage bins are well aerated to prevent moisture migration from warm areas and condensation in cool areas. Either drying fans or bin aeration fans can be used. Aerate at a rate of 0.1 cubic foot per minute per bushel of bin capacity.

In the fall, you should aerate continuously when the outside temperature is 10 to 15 degrees F. cooler than the grain temperature until the grain reaches 40 degrees F. In the winter, aerate for 24 hours every two weeks when the outside temperature is 10 degrees F. higher or lower than grain temperature.

Weeds would not be a problem in balanced soil.

The 24 hours aeration need not be continuous. In the spring, aerate continuously whenever the outside temperature is 10 to 15 degrees F. warmer than grain temperature until grain temperature reaches 60 to 65 degrees F. All of this is made easier if you have automatic controls on your aeration system.

Saving seed. If you want to replant your own seed, save out the needed amount. Seed should be dried to about 13% moisture and kept in ventilated containers (cloth bags, cardboard boxes, or glass jars with cheesecloth covers). It should be stored in a dry, ventilated area at cool temperatures (not higher than 70 degrees F. or lower than 32 degrees F.). Keep away from mice and rabbits.

Seed should maintain a good germination rate for the first year (80 to 85%), but after the second year of storage, germination may drop to 65%. Test the germination rate before planting (See chap. 1).

CHAPTER 5

Uses on the Farm

A lthough most soybean producers strictly grow their beans to sell on the market, high quality soybeans are a valuable source of animal food. It is always better to feed crops you have grown to your animals than to risk buying feed of uncertain origin and quality.

Forage. During the 1930s and 1940s, soybeans were widely grown in the United States for forage and hay. Even though largely superceded by alfalfa, soybeans are an excellent, high protein source of animal feed. Any variety may be grown, but taller indeterminate varieties are best.

If planted for forage or pasture, use a high seeding rate, about 4 to 6 plants per foot in rows about 8 inches apart. Soybeans may also be interplanted with grasses for grazing or with corn or sorghum for a ready-mixed chopped feed. The soybeans are valuable as a soil builder.

Hay. For maximum yield, soybeans for hay should be cut when the seeds have begun to set but before the leaves turn yellow. Cut on a sunny day after the dew is off. Let lie until the leaves are wilted but not brittle (usually the next day). Rake into windrows and let cure for 4 to 5 days. Soybean hay takes longer to cure than other hays, but it is less susceptible to rain damage and can be stored for long periods without nutrient loss. When baling or handling soybean hay, use care to avoid leaf loss.

Soybean hay is similar to alfalfa in nutrient content. It is slightly laxative, and limited amounts should be fed for the first few weeks (it can be mixed with grass hay to reduce amounts). There may be some animal refusal of the hay. Soybean hay should not be available to the animal all the time.

Silage. Soybean plants make a palatable component of silage, at a ratio of two parts corn to one part soybeans. The two crops can be interplanted to facilitate chopping or they can be grown separately and mixed. If interplanted, the seeds can be mixed in the planter and planted at about 20 pounds per acre in corn-width rows. If planted separately, the soybeans should be allowed to wilt after cutting to about 70% moisture. Harvest when the plants are green and succulent.

Other silage seed mixtures that work well are:

3 parts corn	or:	3 parts corn
1 part sorghum		1 part sunflowers
1 part soybeans		1 part soybeans

Feed grain. Raw soybean seeds are difficult to digest because they contain what is called an anti-trypsin factor, a substance that inhibits protein digestion. Also, raw soybeans contain urease, an enzyme that breaks down urea into the more toxic substance ammonia. Both of these are destroyed by heat, so cooked or roasted soybeans are easily digested. One-stomach animals such as pigs, horses, poultry and rabbits must eat cooked soybeans. However, ruminant animals (cattle, sheep and goats) can digest raw soybeans without difficulty, and one-stomach animals can be fed grain mixtures with up to 10% raw soybeans. All animals prefer the taste of cooked soybeans.

The most ready source of processed soybeans for animal feed is the soybean meal that results from beans being processed to extract the oil. Currently, soybean meal is the most commonly used source of protein supplement in animal feed. Heat used in processing destroys most of the anti-nutritional factors. Standard meal is 44% crude protein meal, with the hulls being included as fiber. Since poultry do not digest the hulls, a 48% meal is also available. For use in poultry feed mixtures, soybean meal should be toasted to eliminate all of the anti-nutritional factors. Since soybean protein is low in the amino acid methionine, poultry feed mixtures need a source of it. The amount of soybean meal used in the feed depends on the animal's stage of growth and protein needs for lactation. Vitamin and mineral supplements are often added. Soybean oil is also used in feed mixtures, but generally only if economically feasible.

Whole cooked or roasted soybeans can be a valuable addition to animal feeds. Relatively inexpensive cookers or roasters can be obtained for large batches. For small amounts, you can cook them in the kitchen (simmer fresh beans in a small amount of water for 15 to 20 minutes, or until tender; dried beans must be soaked in cold water 24 hours and simmered 4 to 5 hours). Use them within a few hours or refrigerate. To roast soybeans, put in a 300 degree F. oven until light brown (they may be stored in a closed container for a long time).

If whole soybeans in a feed mixture are ground up, use up the feed within a week to insure freshness. Following are some grain mixtures using whole soybeans for animals on pasture or green hay (from *The Soybean Book.* 1978, pages 159 to 161):

For Lactating Dairy Animals (cows or goats):

75 pounds shelled corn	25 pounds soybeans
75 pounds oats	10 pounds dry molasses
25 pounds wheat	2 pounds salt

For Young Calves (1-6 weeks old):

30 pounds shelled corn   5 pounds bone meal or dry milk solids
10 pounds oats   1 cup salt
10 pounds wheat   4 ounces cod liver oil
10 pounds soybeans

For Young Growing Calves (6 weeks to 6 months):

30 pounds shelled corn   10 pounds soybeans
30 pounds oats   20 pounds dry milk solids
30 pounds wheat

For Older Calves:

100 pounds shelled corn   25 pounds soybeans
50 pounds oats   2 pounds salt
25 pounds wheat

For Non-lactating Goats and Sheep:

50 pounds shelled corn	10 pounds soybeans
20 pounds oats	2 pounds dry molasses
20 pounds wheat	

For Fattening Lambs:

30 pounds shelled corn	1 pound dry molasses
2 pounds soybeans	(grind mixture coarsely)

For Pigs:

65 pounds shelled corn	15 pounds soybeans (preferably roasted)
15 pounds wheat	

For Horses and Mules:

80 pounds oats	10 pounds soybeans
50 pounds shelled corn	2 pounds dry molasses

For Brood Mares with Nursing Foals:

30 pounds oats	10 pounds soybeans
30 pounds wheat	2 pounds dry molasses

For Growing Chickens:

30 pounds ground corn	10 pounds dry milk solids
5 pounds ground soybeans	1 cup salt
(preferably roasted)	½ cup cod liver oil
10 pounds rolled oats	

For Laying Hens:

40 pounds ground corn	10 pounds rolled oats
7 pounds ground soybeans	5 pounds dry milk solids
(preferably roasted)	1 cup salt

Dog or Cat Food:

4 cups cooked, mashed soybeans	½ cup leftover animal fat
2 cups cooked, mashed carrots	1 cup cooked meat or organ meats
1 cup non-fat dry milk powder	(heart, liver, kidney, etc.)

Combine first five ingredients. Add enough broth to moisten well. Can be frozen for storage.

Green manure. Soybeans tilled into the soil when they are green and lush make an excellent green manure. Besides the nitrogen from the root nodules, the rest of the plant adds organic matter and various nutrients to the soil. As mentioned earlier, increased organic matter improves soil structure, water holding capacity, drainage, and has other beneficial aspects. An acre of soybeans can add 175 pounds of nitrogen, 95 pounds of potassium and 20 pounds of phosphorus—and you can use seed you grow yourself.

Soybeans can be planted in late summer or early fall after another crop has been removed. High plant populations are best. Don't worry about weed control. When plants are green but before pods form, till into the upper several inches of soil. If the weather is still warm, they will decompose within six weeks. If a green manure crop is incorporated into the soil in the spring, wait several weeks (until it decomposes) before planting another crop, since the decomposing organic matter temporarily ties up nutrients.

CHAPTER 6

Uses in the Home

As mentioned in Chapter 1, the versatile soybean has many uses as human food. It is used in a large variety of prepared or processed foods. Here we will review ways you or your family can use edible soybeans in the home.

Soybeans contain more protein than lean meat. Two pounds of soybeans supply the protein equivalent of 5 pounds of boneless beef, 15 quarts of milk, 6 dozen eggs or 4 pounds of cheese. Soybean protein is the only complete plant protein; that is, it contains all of the amino acids essential for human health. However, it is somewhat low in the amino acids methionine and cystine, but these can be supplemented by eating whole grains (wheat, rye, brown rice, etc.), fish or casein (milk protein).

Soybeans are low in calories. One serving (one-half cup) has only about 100 calories, far less than a serving of meat. Soybeans are excellent for a diabetic diet, since they contain virtually no starch (1 to 3%; the carbohydrates they do contain are complex sugars).

Soybeans are low in cholesterol, but rich in polyunsaturated fats. They also contain high amounts of lecithin and linoleic acid, which have been shown to lower blood cholesterol levels. The soluble fiber content of soybeans has also been found to help lower cholesterol (the harmful kinds of cholesterol are reduced, not the beneficial kinds that the body needs).

Cooked soybeans are nearly flavorless, allowing them to be blended into many dishes or used as extenders. Many different textures of soybean products are available, from "milk" to paste to flakes to cake to flour. Sprouted soybeans are rich in vitamin C as well as other vitamins and minerals. The cost is very low compared to animal meat—a true nutritional bargain.

Edible varieties. Varieties of soybeans suitable for human food can be obtained from garden seed companies and stores. If you do not want to grow your own, various forms of soybean products can be purchased from health food stores.

Some edible varieties include:

Akita Early. Mature beans are yellow. Fresh beans are ready in 65 days after planting, dried beans in 95 days.

Altona. A good northern variety. Beans are yellow with a black "eye." Fresh beans in 70 days, dried beans in 100 days.

Envoy. A northern variety. Beans are green. Fresh beans in 70 days, dried beans in 104 days.

Meredith. A northern variety. Beans are small and yellow. Fresh beans in 80 days, dried beans in 110 days.

Oriental Black. Mature beans are black. Fresh beans in 70 days, dried beans in 100 days.

Panther. A black, highly digestible variety. Fresh beans in 85 days, dried beans in 115 days.

Prize. A tall variety with large beans adaptable to most areas. Fresh beans in 85 days, dried beans in 115 days.

Traverse. A yellow-beaned northern variety. Fresh beans in 81 days, dried beans in 111 days.

Try to buy varieties adapted to your area. Early varieties do best in the north, and medium or late varieties in the south.

Growing edible soybeans for the commercial market or for local restaurants, health food stores, or tofu makers is an excellent way to greatly increase your per-acre income. Harvesting fresh (green) soybeans cannot easily be done by machine, however, so it would be a labor-intensive crop. A special harvester has been designed for green soybeans, made by Frank Hamachek Machine Company, Kewaunee, Wisconsin 54216. To inquire about marketing, contact INTSOY, University of Illinois, Urbana, Illinois 61801, or contact Consulate General of Japan, 737 N. Michigan Avenue, Chicago, Illinois 60611 or 2520 Massachusetts Avenue N.W., Washington, D.C. 20008.

Here are some ways you can use soybeans as food (from *The Soybean Book*, 1978):

Fresh soybeans. If the beans are picked just after the pod is filled out (when the pod is plump and green), they can be cooked as a green vegetable, similar to lima beans. They can be shelled or cooked in the pod. Their flavor is rich and nutty. They are rich in vitamin A and the B vitamins. For best food value, cook within two hours of picking. Cook in a small amount of salted water for 10 to 20 minutes (or 25 to 30 minutes in the pod—do not eat the pod).

Dried beans. Dried mature beans must first be soaked before cooking. Soak 24 hours in cold water. Refrigeration is necessary to prevent fermentation. Cook beans in their soaking water (it contains vitamins), either simmer for 4 to 5 hours in a saucepan (add water if needed), cook at 15 pounds for one hour in a pressure cooker, or simmer 8 to 12 hours in a slow cooker.

Cooked soybeans can be used sparingly along with grains or other vegetables. They can be mashed and used as an extender in hamburgers and meat loaf. They can be put in a blender and added to bread or cookies.

Roasted soybeans. Dried uncooked soybeans can be spread on shallow trays and roasted lightly in a 300 degree F. oven. They taste like peanuts and can be stored dried for a long time.

Soy grits. Coarsely ground dried soybeans cook in about half the time of whole dried beans (see above) and have a meat-like texture. By adding meat broth and other flavorings (onion, tomato juice, soy sauce), a good meat substitute can be prepared.

Soy flour. Soy flour is a fine powder, rich in protein, with almost no starch or gluten. A small amount in wheat flour (no more than ¼ the amount of wheat flour) will keep bread soft and moist. In cookie, cake and pancake recipes, as much as one-half of the wheat flour may be replaced by soy flour. Lower the oven temperature about 25 degrees F., since soy flour browns more quickly than wheat flour. You can grind your own soy flour, but it is easier to buy it at health food stores. Keep it refrigerated in tight containers.

Soy milk. Resembling cow's milk, soy milk is good for people who cannot digest or are allergic to cow's milk. Soy milk contains as much protein as cow's milk, but less calcium. The easiest way to make soy milk is to gradually stir 8 cups of cold water into 2 cups of soy flour. Let stand for two hours. Heat to simmering in the top of a double boiler, then lower heat, cover and cook 40 minutes. Cool slightly and strain through cheesecloth. Add 4 table-spoons sugar (or honey), 4 tablespoons cooking or salad oil and ½ teaspoon salt; mix thoroughly in a blender. Add cold water to make two quarts soy milk. Keep tightly covered in a refrigerator; use in a few days.

Soy sprouts. Sprouted dried soybeans are a very nutritious fresh vegetable that can be steamed, fried, creamed, or used fresh in salads, soups, stews or casseroles. Sprouts are rich in vitamin C, protein and minerals, and are easy to grow.

One pound of soybeans will produce six pounds of sprouts, enough to serve 35 to 40 people, so use small amounts (one-third cup of beans will produce two cups of sprouts). Rinse the dried beans with water and put into a suitable container (a glass or plastic jar is fine) and cover with water overnight at room temperature. Pour off the water, rinse with fresh water and cover the container with cheesecloth to allow air circulation but retain moisture. Keep in a dark, warm (70 to 80 degrees F.) place for 4 to 5 days. Rinse with fresh water several times a day and turn the container over to stir up the sprouts. Refrigerate 2 to 3 days before eating. Use within 3 to 4 days.

Besides being used fresh or cooked, soy sprouts can also be dried (on a cookie sheet in a dry, well-ventilated place or in a 150 degree F. oven) and chopped or ground. They have a nutty flavor and can be used to add flavor to many foods.

Soy curd (tofu). Soy curd is curdled soy milk made by adding an acid or mineral salts (calcium sulfate) to the milk. You can buy it at health food stores or make your own (use one tablespoon vinegar or lemon juice for each quart of soy milk and leave in a warm place until it thickens; cut into chunks and slowly heat to boiling in a double boiler; cool for 10 minutes and strain out liquid through cheesecloth). The softer curd can be drained or pressed to give a firmer texture, then sliced if desired. Salt, pepper or herbs can be added for flavoring.

When creamed in a blender, soft tofu can be used in salad dressings, puddings, dips, pie fillings and sauces. It makes an excellent, digestible baby food (add vegetables or flavoring). Tofu can replace the eggs in quiche or some or all of the ground beef in meatloaf. Sliced drained tofu can be breaded and fried or baked as a meat substitute. Chunks of tofu can be used in soups, casseroles or stir fries. It can be scrambled like eggs. Frozen tofu has a chewy meaty texture when thawed and squeezed to remove water.

Hundreds of recipes for tofu and other soybean dishes are available from soybean cookbooks and health food stores.

There you have it, a survey of that amazing plant—the soybean—a highly nutritious and useful crop that you can grow even better with proper soil management.

INDEX